Body image,
Boys and
Bible Bits

Kathy Lee

Other books in the Phoebe series:
Fabulous Phoebe
Phoebe's Fortune
Phoebe Finds her Feet

Copyright © Kathy Lee 2003
First published 2003
ISBN 1 85999 663 9

Scripture Union, 207–209 Queensway, Bletchley, Milton Keynes, MK2 2EB, England.
Email: info@scriptureunion.org.uk
Website: www.scriptureunion.org.uk

Scripture Union Australia
Locked Bag 2, Central Coast Business Centre, NSW 2252
Website: www.su.org.au

Scripture quotations are from the Good News Bible/Contemporary English Version published by The Bible Societies/HarperCollins Publishers, copyright © 1966, 1971, 1976, 1992 American Bible Society (CEV)/1991, 1992, 1995 American Bible Society (CEV). Quotes from pages 26, 70 and 82 taken from interviews in J17.

British Library Cataloguing-in-Publication Data.
A catalogue record of this book is available from the British Library.

Printed and bound in Great Britain by Ebenezer Baylis & Son Ltd., Worcester.
Cover design: PRE Consultants Ltd

This is my scrapbook of advice and ideas I've picked up, and my general thoughts on life, boys, God, the universe and other important stuff. I'm Phoebe and I'm 13...

Hear My Prayer

_____ I've been finding out lots _____
of praying quotes/info.

My friends who don't believe in God think that praying is a total waste of time.

"WHY DON'T YOU PRAY TO WIN THE LOTTERY? OR TO MAKE MARK FALL MADLY IN LOVE WITH YOU?"

"YOU COULD ASK GOD TO STOP ALL WARS AND SICKNESS AND HUNGER. BUT HE WON'T DO IT, WILL HE? BECAUSE HE DOESN'T EXIST."

"IT'S POINTLESS PRAYING. WHEN MY PARENTS SPLIT UP, I PRAYED THEY WOULD CHANGE THEIR MINDS . . . BUT IT DIDN'T WORK."

> This is how you should pray:
> Our Father in heaven...
> (Matthew 6)

My own dad wouldn't like it if I never talked to him, except to ask for things.

"DAD, I NEED SOME MONEY AND A LIFT HOME TONIGHT, AND CAN YOU FIX THAT SHELF IN MY BEDROOM, OKAY? BYE!"

God is my Father in heaven, and I can talk to him any time about anything... not just when I want something.

Pray at all times.
(1 Thessalonians 5)

At home or at school, in church or in the cinema or even in the shower, I can talk to God. (Praying is quicker than a text message and cheaper than a mobile.)

giv thanx 2 da Lord coz hes gd. His luv goes on 4eva. Psalm 106:1

Before I pray, I sometimes listen to a worship song. If I'm really getting into it, I have a dance as well. ☺ The music really helps me to come in to God's presence.

I've discovered there are six things I can do when I'm praying.

1 Tell God what he means to me.
2 Tell God I'm sorry.
3 Tell God I'm grateful.
4 Ask God for what I need.
5 Ask God for what others need.
6 Listen to God.

I sometimes try some biblical 'worship body language' that I read about in a book. (Just make sure the window cleaner isn't around first.)

Kneeling down – a sign of respect for God's greatness.

Bowing to the ground – a sign of great awe in God's presence.

Lifting hands – a sign of asking for help.

Clapping – a sign of gratitude, joy and happiness.

Dancing – a way of praising God for what he's done.

God wants us to keep in touch with him and ask him for whatever we need.

(Note: <u>need</u> is not the same as <u>want</u>...)

In all your prayers ask God for what you need, always asking him with a thankful heart.

And God's peace will keep your hearts and minds safe. (Philippians 4)

Sometimes, when I ask for things, God makes them happen straight away. Other times I have to wait.

Sometimes I don't get what I ask for, and I start to think, "What's the good of praying?"
I forget all the times when I did get what I prayed for.

Maybe I should start writing down all the times when my prayers were answered – so that I don't forget.

I'm
Depressed...

I'm not the only one.
Everyone gets depressed sometimes.
Doctors studied 1,000 teenage girls
and found that over half of them
were depressed! I read about
it in the paper.

These are the best years
of our lives.

Not.

(At least I hope not.)

The paper also said that in 1995, 13.2 million
prescriptions were written for antidepressants. Wow!

> The Lord is near to those
> who are discouraged;
> he saves those who have
> lost all hope.
> (Psalm 34)

Really? The Lord is near to me?
Sometimes it's hard to believe...
On those days when everything goes
spectacularly wrong,
On days when no one seems
to like me,
The Lord is near to me?

These are all the things I know are true about God. I'm going to look at this when I feel down.

1. He's promised he isn't going to leave me.
2. He will keep me safe from evil.
3. I needn't be afraid of dying because I'll live with him forever in heaven.
4. He will care for me.
5. Nothing at all can separate me from his love.
6. No one at all can snatch me away from his hand.
7. When I talk to him, he'll listen to me.
8. He forgives me.
9. He loves me.
10. He LIKES me!

> *I am bowed down, I am crushed;*
> *I mourn all day long...*
> *I am like the deaf and cannot hear,*
> *Like the dumb and cannot speak...*
> *Do not abandon me, O Lord!*
> *(Psalm 38)*

GOD, SOMETIMES IT'S JUST TOO HARD TO HEAR YOU OR EVEN TALK TO YOU.

We all get a bit down sometimes, but our youth leader said that if we keep feeling like that, we need to talk to someone we trust about it. There's no need to feel embarrassed or guilty – it's happened to plenty of people.

> I waited patiently for the Lord's help;
> then he listened to me and heard my cry.
> He pulled me out of a dangerous pit,
> Out of the deadly quicksand.
> (Psalm 40)

I've got a bookmark that says:

'Lord, please give me patience...
but hurry up!'

It often feels like it's the hardest
times when I need to be most
patient. Not easy!

God set me safely on a rock
and made me secure.
He taught me to sing a new song,
a song of praise to our God.
Happy are those who trust the Lord!
(Psalm 40)

Praising God
    when I'm depressed
feels harder than running up a
                mountain.
The weird thing is, though, when
        I try it...
    it actually helps!

The Lord is my shepherd;
I have everything I need.
He lets me rest in fields of
green grass, and leads me to
quiet pools of fresh water...
Even if I go through the
deepest darkness,
I will not be afraid, Lord,
For you are with me.
(Psalm 23)

When I actually do PE and get really thirsty I understand this better!

> "There is no pit so
> deep that God is not
> deeper still."

The words of a prisoner in a
Nazi concentration camp.

In all the horror and cruelty
and death, she still managed
to trust in God. And he was
with her through the deepest
darkness... right to the end.

Bad Hair,
Bad Face,
Bad Everything
Day

Sometimes I really hate the way I look.
I stare at myself in the mirror
and wish I was completely different.

- Thinner.

- Better skin.

- Nicer eyes.

- Longer legs.

In fact, from my hair to my toenails,
there's nothing I would keep.
I would change the lot!

(Except my elbows. I have lovely elbows.)

Q Why does everyone in magazines always look perfect?

A They don't! All their spots have been airbrushed out!

When my bones were being formed,
carefully put together in my
mother's womb,
when I was growing there in secret
you knew that I was there –
you saw me before I was born.
(Psalm 139)

"No one loves me" is a lie; I have to keep remembering that. God loves me – good or bad, fat or thin. He thinks I'm beautiful!

GOD MUST LOVE ORDINARY PEOPLE –
HE MADE SO MANY OF US.

He could have made everyone in
the world amazingly handsome or
beautiful.
But he didn't.

Man looks at the outward
appearance, but I look
at the heart.
(1 Samuel 16)

"Perfection for me is somebody who's completely
comfortable with all their imperfections."

Justin Timberlake, singer

Sometimes I look in the mirror and pick two things I like about myself. It helps me when I'm having a bit of a downer.

"Man looks at the outward appearance..."
Too right he does. And <u>man</u> includes <u>boys</u>.
Boys always look at the outward appearance...
I'll never get a boyfriend, looking like this!

Maybe I should advertise:

> **LIVELY**, outgoing girl, good sense of humour, would like to meet short-sighted boy.
> **PS** I don't care what you look like.

Did you spot the tiny white lie?
Actually I <u>do</u> care what people look like.
Could I fancy a boy with loads of spots,
huge ears or greasy hair?
Even if he was a really nice person?

Charm is deceptive
And beauty disappears
(Proverbs 31)

**Don't judge a book by
the cover
(My mum's proverbs no 1)**

I've discovered a brilliant hair care
tip: lemon juice! Works really well
on blonde hair.

Love your neighbour as you love yourself.
But if you treat people according to their outward appearance, you are guilty of sin.
(James 2)

So I should try to be nice
to everyone –
the good, the bad and the ugly?

Hmm... easier said than done.

"Looks may open doors – but they don't keep you in the room."
Brad Pitt, actor

> *You are the people of God;*
> *he loved you and chose you*
> *for his own.*
> *(Colossians 3)*

God loves me... and he doesn't care what I look like.

But he does care about what I am like on the inside. That's what really matters...

— The book, not the cover.

— The food, not the packaging.

I really should spend more time listening to God and reading what he has to say about me.

I Wish I Hadn't Done That . . .

Today I'd give anything to be able to go back in time.

I want to undo what I just did and unsay what I said. It was wrong, I know it was.

Now I feel terrible.
Guilty.
Ashamed.
Everyone must hate me.
I bet even God hates me!

I recognise my faults;
I am always conscious of my sins.
I have sinned against you
and done what you consider evil.
So you are right in judging me
(Psalm 51)

I'm REALLY sorry.
I wish I hadn't done it.
But it's too late... I can't go
back and change things.

I know I should 'confess' what I did, but I'm too embarrassed.

I think I might write down everything I'm sorry about, and hand it to God.

Dear Father,

I really blew it again today.

I ....
....
I've got no excuses and I won't try to wriggle
out of taking responsibility for my actions. I
agree with you that what I did was wrong.
Please forgive me and help me to cut this
problem right out of my life.

Finally, Father, I want to thank you that you
are so kind and generous that even as I
confess this sin you have forgiven and
forgotten completely. Thanks that you can
forgive more times than I can sin!

Love, Phoebe

Create a pure heart in me, O God,
and put a new and loyal spirit
in me...
Give me the joy that comes from
your salvation.
(Psalm 51)

...and help me not to make the
same mistake again.

TOP TIP

Nothing is ever so bad that
I can't talk to God about it.

*You take pleasure in showing us
your constant love...
You will trample our sins
underfoot and send them to the
bottom of the sea!
(Micah 7)*

That's amazing!
God may hate the wrong things I've
done, but he doesn't hate <u>me.</u>

And if I ask him to forgive me...
he does.

He says, "I will not
remember their sins and
evil deeds any longer."
(Hebrews 10)

God forgets the wrong things I did!
He just wipes them out completely,
as if they never happened!

Everyone

Else Does

It . . .

EVERYONE ELSE IS ALLOWED TO ...

ALL MY FRIENDS HAVE GOT ONE ...

I DON'T WANT TO FEEL LEFT OUT.

I don't want to look like a six-year-old with over-anxious parents.

I don't want my friends to think they're growing up and leaving me behind.

It's so unfair!

Everyone else does it!

"I'll be the horrible parent who'll check up on you. But I'll be reasonable too. And I'll always stand with you." Dad

Mum asks me, "If everyone else jumped over a cliff, would you do it too?"

☐ A: Yes, if it looked like they were having a good time on the way down.

☐ B: Yes, because I'd be so lonely without any friends left.

☐ C: No, because my mum would make me wait until I'm older.

> *Be careful how you live...*
> *These are evil days.*
> *Try to find out what the Lord*
> *wants you to do.*
> *(Ephesians 5)*

That's what I need to know.
Not what my friends want me to do,
or even what my parents want.
What does God want me to do?

I can look in the Bible. It's God's advice to me, and is the best way to find out what he wants me to do. I'm going to give *One Up* notes a try — they get me to read small chunks of the Bible and think about them. I think I can manage that...

Since you are God's dear children,
you must try to be like him.
(Ephesians 5)

I always try to think what Jesus
would do if he was here.
(My mum's proverbs no 2)

Well, yes... sometimes that helps.

And sometimes it doesn't.

The hardest thing is, I don't like being different from everyone else. I want to fit in with my friends. I want to belong.

You used to be in the darkness, but since you have become the Lord's people, you are in the light.
So you must live like people who belong to the light.
(Ephesians 5)

Young people, enjoy your youth...
Do what you want to do, and
follow your heart's desire.
But remember that God is going to
judge you for whatever you do.
(Ecclesiastes 11)

God
isn't like a strict
head teacher, forbidding all
kinds of things just because we
might enjoy them.
He loves us, he wants the best for us.
He wants us to be like him.

Let God transform you inwardly...
Then you will be able to know
what is good and pleasing to him
and perfect.
(Romans 12)

Sometimes I feel as if dozens of
voices are shouting in my ears.

MY FRIENDS   MY PARENTS

WHAT I WANT
=

Help me, God, to hear your voice
clearly and to do what you say.

Happy Days

Things that make me feel happy.

- Orange Club biscuits.
- Compliments.
- School days when I don't have PE.
- Big Macs.
- Sunny days.
- Sleep.
- My hair.

In Science, we talked about what teenage hormones do to you. They change everything – including your emotions.
Your feelings swoop up and plunge down again like a roller-coaster ride.
Good days are incredible. Bad days are the absolute pits.
Today's a good day.
Better make the most of it, before the roller-coaster sweeps me downwards again.

When I feel really great, it makes me want to sing out loud. If people give me funny looks (and they do), I just sing quietly to myself. And to God.

> I will sing to the Lord
> all my life...
> May he be pleased with my song,
> for my gladness comes from him.
> (Psalm 104)

*Praise the Lord, my soul,
and do not forget how kind he is...
He fills my life with good things.*
(Psalm 103)

Thank you, Lord, for all the good
things in my life. There are so many,
I can't count them all.

I'm going to write down a list
of all the good things in my life
and look at it when I'm down.

O Lord, my God, how great you are!
You use the clouds as your chariot
and ride on the wings of the
wind...
You make springs flow in the
valleys
and rivers run between the hills.
In the trees nearby
the birds make their nests and
sing.
(Psalm 104)

Thank you for creating the world. And for taking care of it, in spite of the way people try to mess it up.

God rules over the whole earth,
from the deepest caves to
the highest hills...
He is our God;
we are the people he cares for,
the flock for which he provides.
(Psalm 95)

Even as you rule over the universe,
you find time to think about us...
about me.

That's AMAZING!

Jesus, you are special to me because…

1..

2..

3..

Jesus, I want to worship you today because

....

....

....

....

....

Maybe I'm Adopted . . .

Sometimes I feel as if I really don't belong in my own family.

— They don't like the things I like.
— They disagree with what I say.
— They hate my clothes and they absolutely *loathe* my kind of music.

Maybe they adopted me at a very young age and haven't had the courage to tell me.

(But then why do I have hair like Dad's and eyes like Mum's? Hmmm.)

What would my ideal family be like?

1 No kid sister. (Bye-bye, Georgie.)

2 An older brother with dozens of good-looking friends.

3 Rich parents who let me do whatever I like.

4 Grandparents with a holiday home in Florida or somewhere.

You can choose your friends,
but you don't have much choice
about your family.
(My mum's proverbs no 3)

It looks like I'm stuck with the
family I've got. But maybe I can
drop them a few hints on how to
improve themselves...

Hang on. At youth group, they said
your family aren't your choice;
they're God's. God must have landed
me with this bunch for some purpose!

Parents, do not irritate
your children,
or they will become
discouraged.
(Colossians 3)

SEE, DAD! IT'S IN THE BIBLE. DON'T IRRITATE YOUR CHILDREN . . . DON'T NAG ME ABOUT MY HOMEWORK. DON'T CRITICISE MY FAVOURITE TV PROGRAMME. DON'T TELL CORNY JOKES WHEN MY FRIENDS ARE AROUND. JUST DON'T, OKAY?

But Dad came back at me
with another verse:

> *Children, it is*
> *your Christian duty*
> *to obey your parents always,*
> *for that is what pleases God.*
> *(Colossians 3)*

I'm not so keen on that one.
Always? Even in the little things that
they'll never get to hear about? ↘

1 Bunking off Games lessons.
2 Watching that programme they don't want me to see
  in my room instead.
3 Doing last-minute homework on the bus.
4 Sneaking off to use the upstairs phone without asking
  first.
5 Watching '15' certificate videos at my friend's house.

And then there's my sister.
Sometimes I can't stand her.
We have huge arguments over stupid little
things, like the best seat on the sofa.
It's so childish!
I wish she would grow up a bit.

> *Keep on loving one another*
> *as Christian brothers.*
> *(Hebrews 13)*

That's okay. It says <u>brothers</u>,
not <u>sisters</u>...

> *Don't go to bed angry.*
> *(Ephesians 4)*

> *The start of an argument is like the first break in a dam; stop it before it goes any further.*
> *(Proverbs 17)*

Maybe I'll try that next time a quarrel starts. I won't argue back... I'll just smile serenely and let her have what she wants.
Ha! That will _really_ annoy her.

But really, I know I shouldn't wind her up. Sorry, God.

Best

Friends

Your best friend is over the moon because a boy she's liked for ages has finally asked her out. How do you feel?

☐ You're really happy for her... honest.

☐ You envy her (what has she got that you haven't?) but do your best to look pleased.

☐ You're afraid her boyfriend will break up your friendship. You point out all his faults, hoping she'll go off him.

Your friend tells you a secret, making you promise not to pass it on. Do you:

☐ Keep silence for ever.

☐ Tell just one other person, making her promise to keep quiet.

☐ Tell a few people (in strictest confidence) then wonder why your friend has stopped speaking to you.

Psalm 141;
James 3

Your friend wants to go shopping. You would rather go to the cinema. Who wins?

☐ You can usually manage to persuade her to do what you want.

☐ She always gets her own way – she's totally selfish.

☐ You agree to go to the shops this week and the cinema next week.

Ephesians 5

The only way to have a friend
is to be one.
(My mum's proverbs no 4)

Do for others what you want
them to do for you.
(Matthew 7)

"Do unto others before
they do you in!"
Quote from film

- A good friend is patient and kind.

- A good friend is not jealous or proud, selfish or irritable.

- A good friend never gives up.

Of course I want my friends to be like that. Does that mean I have to be like that myself?

> *Everyone must be quick to listen, but slow to speak and slow to become angry.*
> *(James 1)*

Quick to listen, slow to speak... often I get this the wrong way round.

— A good friend is a good listener, right?

— A good friend takes time to really understand people.

> *Gossip is spread by wicked people;*
> *they stir up trouble and break*
> *up friendships.*
> *(Proverbs 16)*

A good friend knows a lot about me, but doesn't tell my secrets to anyone else. (Especially not the things that make me curl up with embarrassment.)

I can trust her.
Can she trust me?

Q "Have you ever blabbed any secrets?"
A "I've got a big mouth so I probably have!"

Jade Goody, *Big Brother* housemate

I Don't

Understand

Boys . . .

It's weird.

When I was in Junior School, boys seemed quite ordinary. They weren't that different from girls. I could talk to them about lots of things (except football).

But now, boys and girls are totally different. They talk about different things, they read different magazines, they like different music.

> "We all live with the objective of being happy; our lives are all different and yet the same."
>
> Anne Frank

Boys read magazines about:

Football • Computer games • Bikes
Motor racing • Fishing • Climbing
Skateboards • Martial arts.

Girls read magazines about:

Fashion • Friendships • Films • Make-up
Pop stars • Boyfriends • Problems
Boyfriend problems...

"Few women admit their age.
Few men act theirs."

Unknown

Girls have started growing up while all the boys in their year are still like little kids.

Boys are _so_ immature!
They laugh at the stupidest things...

- Whoopee cushions.
- Jackie Chan films.
- Useless teachers.
- Squashed hedgehogs.
- Girls they don't like.

Boys muck about in school. They seem to think it's not cool to be clever.

They don't do any work, their homework is a mess, they don't revise for tests.

But maybe boys have more fun?

According to a website I looked at, 46% of boys got 5 or more grades A*-C at GCSE in 2000/01. 57% of girls got the same. Interesting!

Boys get obsessions about things...

- Man United.
- *Star Trek.*
- Formula One.
- Skateboarding.
- Every record Nirvana ever made.
- Highest ever score on some crummy computer game.

Girls have better things to do with their time.

IS EASTENDERS ON YET?

Me and my friend have a system
for grading boys – like GCSEs.

A – Absolutely Adorable.
B – Better than most.
C – Could be okay, if...
D – Don't bother.
E – Excruciating.
F – Friend of Frankenstein.

I know I
shouldn't say that kind of
thing, but it's hard not to.

- Boys are stupid and immature, obsessive and careless and a total waste of time.
- Boys aren't nearly as nice as girls.
- Boys have a cruel sense of humour.
- Boys smell.

But I could forgive them for
everything...
if only some boy, somewhere, sometime
would ask me out!

A Heavy Problem

Q

Why do I want to lose weight?

A

- To impress my friends.
- To stop people making nasty comments about the way I look.
- So that boys fancy me.
- To feel fitter and healthier.
- So I can buy clothes that don't look like circus tents.
- So that plastic chairs don't creak alarmingly when I sit down.
- So I can be happy.

Being thin doesn't automatically mean being happy
(My mum's proverbs no 5)

Yes, actually I know a few thin people who are totally miserable.
I also know of fat people who seem quite happy, such as Father Christmas.

(but who wouldn't be happy if they only worked one day a year?)

I sometimes feel as if losing weight would solve all my problems instantly. I would turn into a different person – confident, attractive, popular.
I would be the one all the other girls envy.

In reality I bet it wouldn't happen. Even if I was thin, I would still be me.

"I want a girl who'll eat a Whopper with me and be happy. It bugs me when chicks are food wimps. Skinny is not sexy to me at all."
Justin Timberlake, singer

To hide a big bum:

1 Wear long rugby tops, big jumpers or tracky bottoms.

2 Avoid wall-to-wall mirrors.

3 Never turn around.

Does it matter to God whether I'm fat or thin?

> I am certain that nothing can separate us from God's love.
> (Romans 8)

God will always love me, whatever I look like... fat or thin, ugly or beautiful, old or young.

But that doesn't mean I should stop caring about my weight problem...

> Not everything is good for
>   you...
> I am not going to let
> anything make me its slave
> (1 Corinthians 6)

If someone leaves a half-opened packet of biscuits around, I can't resist eating a few. But that doesn't mean I'm addicted... does it?

> Your body is the temple of
> the Holy Spirit, who lives
> in you... So use your body
> for God's glory
> (1 Corinthians 6)

That's an amazing
thought. God's Holy Spirit actually
lives in me!

I sometimes hate my body. I think of
it as fat and ugly. And yet God's
Spirit lives there...
I ought to take care of my body
and not mess it around.

> *Do not live as your human nature*
> *tells you to; instead, live as*
> *God's Spirit tells you to.*
> *(Romans 8)*

When my hand keeps reaching out for the
biscuit tin, and my taste buds tell me,
"Just one more Jaffa cake won't hurt,"
that's human nature talking.

I should try to listen to God's
Spirit instead.

**SOMEHOW, ADDICTIONS TO
CIGARETTES/DRUGS/ALCOHOL
SEEM WORSE THAN ADDICTIONS TO
FOOD/EXERCISE . . . I WONDER WHY?**

Telling the Future

Q

What do you want to be when you grow up?

A

Age 2:   A doggy
Age 4:   A princess
Age 6:   A nurse
Age 8:   An air hostess
Age 10:   An actress
Age 11:   An author
Age 12:   Rich and famous
Now: Don't know

God's answer: Loved by me!

At school we heard about predictions people made in the 1950s about what life would be like after the year 2000. They thought we'd be driving rocket-powered cars by now!

I haven't a clue what I want to be. And soon I'm going to have to make some decisions that might affect my whole life. What school subjects should I choose?

French or German?

Art, Drama or Music?

IT or Food Technology?

Whatever I choose, I may be sorry later on and wish I'd chosen something different.

I really wish I could see
into the future.

All sorts of people try to do it...
Horoscope writers.
Weather forecasters.
The Financial Times.
Environmental
scientists.
Religious maniacs.

They all say they know what will
happen - and they all get it wrong.

Even before I speak,
you already know what
I will say.
(Psalm 139)

Only God can
see into the future.
He knows all about us, from our
earliest days to our old age.

The Lord says, "I will teach you
the way you should go;
I will instruct you and advise you."
(Psalm 32)

> *If any of you lack wisdom,*
> *you should pray to God, who*
> *will give it to you.*
> *(James 1)*

I do need wisdom... not only for the big decisions, like what to do with my life.

I need wisdom to make lots of little choices, everyday decisions.

"We were teenagers once, too! Maybe we regret some of the decisions we made and we want you to learn from that." Mum

"Don't sell yourself short. You are worth a lot." Teacher

"You only get one shot at this, so be as wise as you can be with the years you've got." Dad

> *Your Father in heaven knows what you need... Do not worry about tomorrow.*
> *(Matthew 6)*

It's no good worrying about the future. That's like trying to mop up a spilt drink before you've even spilt it.

> **Worry can't change yesterday or tomorrow, but it can ruin today.**
> **(My mum's proverbs no 6)**

I worry about going to the dentist, but it won't make the drill any quieter or the pink mouthwash taste like strawberry milkshake!

Leave all your worries with him,
because he cares for you.
(1 Peter 5)

When I feel worried, I can pray
about the problem, then leave it in
God's hands.

God is our God for ever
and ever;
he will lead us for all
time to come.
(Psalm 48)

7 Favourite Healthy Snacks

Instead of sweets – seedless grapes
Instead of crisps – bowl of corn flakes
Instead of pizza – ham salad sandwich
Instead of milkshake – Diet Coke
Instead of orange Club biscuit – an orange
Instead of ice cream – strawberry yoghurt
Instead of chips – jacket potato with tuna

Better still – instead of eating, phone a friend, do some exercise, use the computer, take the dog out…

9 Favourite
Bible Bits

When I feel depressed   Matthew 11 v 28
When I'm happy   Psalm 100
When I'm angry   Romans 12 v 17-21
When I'm lonely   Psalm 23
When I'm scared   Psalm 57 v 1-3
When I feel guilty   Psalm 51 v 1-7
When God seems far away   Psalm 139 v 7-13
When I'm not sure
  what to do   Psalm 32 v 6-8
To know what true love is   1 Corinthians 13